CELLO TIM[E]

Seven Pieces in First Position for the elementa[ry]

Violoncello

1. String Along

2. Lazy Days

No part of this publication may be copied or reproduced in any form or by any means without the prior permission of Novello & Company Limited.

© Copyright 1988 Novello & Company Limited   Order No: NOV 120641   All Rights Reserved

3. Scale Play

4. Morning Dew-ette

5. Ikrania Dance

6. Theme for Two

VIOLONCELLO

7. Frog Dance

Lightly and energetically ♩. = 80

Published by Novello Publishing Ltd
Printed in Great Britain by Headway Press Ltd

9/00 (38283)

COLIN EVANS

CELLO TIME

Seven pieces in First Position
for the elementary cello player
with piano accompaniment

The cello part is inserted

Order No: NOV 120641

NOVELLO PUBLISHING LIMITED
8/9 Frith Street, London W1V 5TZ

Percy Prior's
£ 6.95

CELLO TIME

COLIN EVANS

1. String Along

© Copyright 1988 Novello & Company Limited

All Rights Reserved

No part of this publication may be copied or reproduced in any form or by any means without the prior permission of Novello & Company Limited

2. Lazy Days

3. Scale Play

4. Morning Dew-ette

5. Ikrania Dance

6. Theme for Two

With flowing movement ♩ = 108

7. Frog Dance

Lightly and energetically ♩. = 80

12